Freedom
Is A Gift
Are You
Worth It?

Freedom Is A Gift Are You Worth It?

Would You Give Your Life for The Freedom of Others? A Marine Recovery Patrol Becomes a Lesson in Selfless Dedication.

By Tad Pritchett

*Freedom Is a Gift Are You Worth
It? Would You Give Your Life For
The Freedom of Others?*

*By Tad Pritchett
VIETVET.US*

*Molly Luvblossum Press
Lenexa, KS*

*Published 2020
Copyright Tad Pritchett 2020*

ISBN--978-0-9976529-2-5

Special Thanks

Special thanks to my wife Dee Pritchett and my dear friend Dave Murray. Their advice and diligent editing have been invaluable.

A special recognition to my long-time Vietnam Veteran friends Dan Sullivan, Jesse Randall and Frank Brown.
Semper Fidelis

Table of Contents

TAKE THE PLEDGE

- I am responsible for myself and accountable for my behaviors.

- I will not be defined by failure and I will never quit.

- I will never settle for my best effort.

- I will create a supportive environment where my friends build pride and confidence in each other.

- I will always balance my mind and heart.

INTRODUCTION
THE VALUE OF VETERANS

When I was a kid, it was called "Armistice Day," named after the Armistice ending WWI on 11 November 1918, to recognize WWI Veterans. More wars made more Veterans, so in 1954 it was renamed Veterans Day to honor Veterans of all wars. It provides a method for all Americans to recognize and honor their Veterans. Why is it important that we recognize Veterans and what is appropriate? What can we learn from our Veterans?

Hundreds of years ago, people from all over the world came to what would become America for one reason: Freedom. They wanted to choose their own churches, raise their families according to their own values and to pursue their own fortunes. They wanted Freedom of choice to follow their dreams, the right to "life, liberty and the pursuit of happiness," within a framework of laws <u>THEY</u> created.

What does that mean for us? It means we can go to school and learn how to think for ourselves, play sports, have our own friends and be with our families. We can worship as we want and raise our families according to our own values. We have FREEDOM to make choices in our lives that define our homes and communities, take different paths with different behaviors and thoughts. We have Freedom to live our lives the way we choose, <u>freedom of choice</u>.

Americans have the right of free speech and assembly and with that right comes the responsibility for our own actions. That means we can speak out freely against our leaders without fear of retribution. We can gather with others to support or protest for our best interests, but we are accountable for how we behave.

We also benefit from other American's freedom to pursue their dreams to make a better world for us, each dream spawning new dreams. Every aspect of freedom is intertwined and dependent upon other freedoms, it is not unilaterally aligned with itself. Freedom's survival depends upon the integration of all of our dreams. Our way of life is driven by the interdependence of choices and the responsible choices we all make to better the lives of all Americans. We cannot deny access to America's freedoms to anyone, our freedoms are interconnected.

We have the right to protest but outrage on social media is low risk, it is "virtual courage." It does not require a physical presence, nor does it draw on the courage required by physical presence. Simply said, one cannot turn over a car with an iPhone nor has an iPhone served any jail time. Action is not manifested through an anonymous third-person keyboard.

Is Social Media creating a gap between the reality of action and the "virtually perceived" reality of action? As a result, are we viewing our social system as a service arrangement where people can purchase services without appreciating the providers' skills and experience? In other words, social media is taking the place of meaningful, personal, one-on-one interaction where we physically express ourselves and learn about others. To a large extent it has undermined courage.

Overlay this thought of "virtually perceived" reality of action with another. In our schools, history is no longer a respected body of study, programs have become casualties of budget cuts and self-interests. I love to do presentations for young Americans and, as I go to elementary, middle and high schools, I learn that I am there because the history programs have left out a lot of my, and previous generation's history. I am there to teach, to put a face on the reality of history.

Veterans have offered their lives for us and I use my Vietnam War experience as a vehicle to teach the value of Veterans in our history. As our country moved to an all-volunteer military, the military is no longer enmeshed into everyday America and the commercialization of our Veterans dilutes the message of sacrifice and accomplishments.

Just as social media has pushed us into an anonymous third-person world, I worry that our youth is viewing our wonderful all-volunteer military personnel as a third-party service, offering their lives for their freedom.

We have doctors, electricity, water, furniture and a choice of automobiles. Virtually everything we touch, see, hear or feel happens because of our freedom to pursue our dreams. But freedom is a facade supported only by constant vigilance and defense against erosion from those who want to put us into a subservient position.

Since the Declaration of Independence, Americans have given their minds, their bodies and their lives for an idea, a thought, a feeling. Freedom, the American right to make choices and follow our dreams.

Freedom must be earned and protected by every generation of Americans. We must protect it, fight for it, and bequeath it to the next generation for them to step up to the same challenges. We call these defenders of FREEDOM military "Veterans." Veterans believe from the depths of their souls, that your FREEDOM to choose is more important than their lives. A Veteran gives you the GIFT OF FREEDOM.

American Veterans have kept that dream alive giving their minds, their bodies and their lives for an idea, a thought, a feeling, FREEDOM! Freedom, the American right to make choices and to follow our dreams. We cannot become complacent and take these FREEDOMS for granted. It is now your turn to step up.

Veterans have given their blood, sweat and tears. They have not provided us with a service as a plumber might come to our home and fix a leaky faucet. We <u>pay</u> for a service, but Veterans have <u>given</u> us a gift, the gift of Freedom and we have accepted that gift every day by living in America. So instead of saying "thank you for your service," we should say "thank you for my FREEDOM."

This is the story of a patrol in the Vietnam War that encapsulates why we should all honor and love Veterans for their sacrifices. Their purpose is to give us the gift of Freedom and teach us how to use it. What are our obligations? How do we honor them? What can we learn from them? They have a purpose in your life, and it is your DUTY to discover and learn.

FREEDOM IS A GIFT, ARE YOU WORTH IT? This is my fourth book challenging young Americans to grow up! I recount my war experiences not for the story but for the "if I can do this, so can you," example and to put a face on Veterans' experiences. This is the actual story of twenty-three-year-old Marine Second Lieutenant Roberts, leading a patrol of teenagers, fighting for the nebulous FREEDOM of our country and for your right to live with that FREEDOM.

Woven into the story are my tenets for growing up, advice to a young audience on how to make responsible choices and to be successful adults. ***Honor our Veterans by taking this pledge:***

TAKE THE PLEDGE
1. I am responsible for myself and accountable for my behaviors.
2. I will not be defined by failure and I will <u>never</u> quit.
3. I will never settle for my best effort.
4. I will create a supportive environment where my friends build pride and confidence in each other.
5. I will always balance my mind and heart.

Author's Note

War is horrible and the combatants are exposed to the worst humanity has to offer. To cope with those horrors, the young combatants rely on a cruel language to communicate with each other. It is a language that disparages every aspect of their behaviors, denigrates each other and dehumanizes the enemy. War language is a dialect conveying very specific emotions and descriptions and one must be in the situation to fully appreciate the tapestry of the verbiage.

This is a book that uses a war story to send a message of principles to young adults and I am reluctant to dilute that important message for the sake of accuracy of language. For that reason, you will not learn that many four-letter words can be used as a noun, verb, adjective or adverb. You will not learn that Marines had derogatory names for each other and the enemy. But you will learn the history of the hardships endured by America's youth when they put on the uniform of a United States Marine and went to war.

In addition to the language, I have changed the term "Gook," to "Charley." "Gook" is a derogatory, demeaning term that combat Marines have used to refer to the enemy for decades. I firmly believe that it is our Constitutional obligation to support, not obstruct, every American in their pursuit of their dreams and demeaning them can only interfere with their access to their rights. Additionally, the 1960's was a different time and we cannot judge the past based upon today.

"Charley" comes from the phonetic spelling of VC, Victory Charley for Viet Cong. The Viet Cong was the political segment of the Communists and fought alongside the North Vietnamese Army. So, I have used "Charley" as the enemy.

As I complete this work we are in the midst of the Corona Virus global pandemic, my wife and I are in "lock down" in our home venturing out every two weeks for necessities. As businesses are closed and people lose their jobs, I can clearly see how our whole way of life and econonmy depend upon everyone's freedom

"Virtually everything we touch, see, hear or feel happens because of our freedom to pursue our dreams."

We are experiencing the loss of freedom to live as we choose. We must protect it with our lives.

Chapter 1

THE RECONS

Marine Second Lieutenant Roberts was standing alone in a Monsoon rain on a jungle-covered mountain top along the border between the Republic of South Vietnam and Laos in Southeast Asia. It was south of an area known as the A Shau Valley.

The Marines were on a multi-regimental sized operation to stop the enemy's flow of troops and supplies. The enemy supply route that snaked from North Vietnam and branched into South Vietnam was called the Ho Chi Minh Trail.

As he sipped his favorite coffee, chocolate, sugar and creamer mix, the day started out much like every other jungle day, hot and very humid with a hint that the enemy was close, watching and like a cat, awaiting any sign of weakness to pounce. It was Monsoon season and rain integrated itself into every aspect of life.

It was letter writing time, between downpours that always soaked the most well-intentioned letters home. His letters home stressed how safe he was and how much he missed home. How was his ten-month-old son, how was his Mom and Dad and how are you, he would ask his young wife? The ritual was always the same. He folded the letter, slipped it into a red, white and blue striped envelope and sealing it after he licked the disgusting glue.

After he printed the address and wrote "Free" where the stamp should go, he then slipped it into a plastic power supply bag and into his pack where it would sit with other letters awaiting a helicopter to ferry them to an FPO (Fleet Post Office) for mailing home.

The last time they had actually talked was when he first arrived in Vietnam and it was by way of the Seabees MARS (Military Auxiliary Radio System) communication station. MARS was a radio telephone call through amateur radio operators in the States and since it was a military communication system, they both had to follow radio protocol by adding "Over" when either of them finished a statement. The MARS station was connected to other stations all over Vietnam so not only was it a stilted military call, it was not private, so terms of affection went like this:

"Miss you so much, over." There was a long pause as his voice made its way through the series of radio transmissions. Because of the time difference it was 3 AM in the States and it was not uncommon for the loved one to go to bed, too sleepy to talk. As Roberts tried to utilize his allotted five minutes, the defensive perimeter of the combat base was probed by the enemy and the call was interrupted by automatic weapons fire, transmitted back to the States. It was not a good call and brought chuckles of sarcasm from the audience at each station in Vietnam.

As the darkness turned to daylight and the Company had completed the morning "Stand to," the Gunny (Company Gunnery Sergeant) appeared by the Lieutenant's foxhole and dropped down into a squat.

"Sir, have you ever heard of an allotment Annie?" Roberts shook his head, no, he had never heard the term.

"They are women who live around our bases and meet our Marines during their basic training. They take them in, act like they are almost married to them and then get them to sign over their allotment checks to them." Allotments are a sum of money that a Marine might get as part of his pay for being married or that the Marine might have taken out of his paycheck to be sent to someone. Either way, it is money leaving the Marine's hands and going to "Allotment Annie."

The Gunny handed the Lieutenant a handwritten letter, obviously in a woman's hand because it was readable. It was from a woman who lived in the town outside of the Camp Lejeune Marine Corps Base in eastern North Carolina who was asking one of his Marines to please have his allotment paid to her.

She went on and on in the letter about how much she loved him and what they would do when he returned. Of course, in reality, she would be nowhere to be found when he returned home. Annie's often would have ten or twenty Marines on the hook at one time, collecting all of their allotments.

It was signed coyly, "Debbie" with the dot on the "i" circled. Roberts looked to see who the lucky Marine was.

"Dearest Howie," he read out loud. He looked at the Gunny. "Is this the Howie I think it is?"

"Yes Sir, it's Pig Pen and you need to talk to him. This woman will bleed him dry."

"Get Pig Pen to my pos (position) ASAP." Pig Pen was a tall, skinny kid from the Appalachia area of Tennessee who got his name because he was always dirty and scruffy like the Peanuts character. His thin red hair blew in the slightest wind and he squeaked when he talked. But he was a very good leader and deceivingly strong with the endurance of a horse. He never seemed to wear down, energizing those he led. Don't judge the book by the cover thought Roberts.

He showed Pig Pen the letter and told him what the scam was. Pig Pen's face sagged in disappointment, his eyes blinking hard.

"Debbie is different, Sir, she really loves me, she told me so many times. She even gave me a picture." The blood thirsty Annie could have been mistaken for a small circus gorilla.

After nearly an hour of conversation, Pig Pen agreed to break off his relationship with Debbie. Another small step toward failure averted and Pig Pen returned to his foxhole, esteem intact.

For nearly two months, the Company had patrolled the jungle trails looking for the enemy, surviving on canned food called C-rations or MCI's (Meal Combat Individual) brought in by supply helicopters. The Company of four platoons was encamped deep in the jungle on Hill 555, a fire support base (FSB) fifteen kilometers from Laos on the Ho Chi Minh Trail. The six 105 mm howitzers and three 155 mm big guns were in direct support of the infantry and moved from one spot to another by helicopters.

As the Lieutenant sat in his muddy foxhole on the slope of the steep hill, he watched his Marines prepare for the day. All kids, yes, and except for Gramps, the oldest was 19, many drafted, not volunteers. Gramps earned his name when turned 20 years old. Unlike today's all volunteer military, many of America's warriors were forced into the military through the draft. Military service during The Vietnam War was mandatory.

Each Marine had a nickname, a way to dehumanize the agony of Vietnam. Twenty-eight Marines in fourteen foxholes that he checked every two to four hours day and night. Of the fourteen holes he had visual contact with half of them.

The C-ration coffee mix was hot in his aluminum canteen cup, heated by a heat tablet and it was his first drink of the day. He had thankfully graduated from a "Boot" stove to a clean burning heat tab fueled stove. New Marines, or Boots (Boot Camp) did not understand that they needed to cut large ventilation holes in a bottom of the can and they had to be large enough for the heat tablet to fully ignite. The smell was suffocating.

As they began to prepare their C-ration breakfasts, he smiled as Turtle and Marbles pooled their Mexican ingredients for a spicy dish.   They manned the hole to his front. Turtle was from

Guadalajara, Mexico by way of Texas and a wonderful Marine. He had bypassed the citizenship hurdles and joined the Marines hoping his military service would help him become an American citizen. In his words, "I love America, I want to be an American." Turtle was one of the most hard-working, considerate people Roberts had ever met and he loved the lime green NVA (North Vietnamese Army) scarf he wore, captured from a dead enemy soldier.

Marbles was from Puerto Rico but lived in Philadelphia when he was drafted. He had a big mustache and his bug eyes made him look like Jerry Colona, an actor who rolled his huge eyes every time he spoke, like Marbles. Before Vietnam he ran a movie house in New York City and complained and lamented about how he would have to compete with the new pornography in movie theaters. Marbles was always helping others and volunteered for everything.

In the next hole was Gambler from Connecticut who loved to go to gambling casinos, a New England tradition handed down from the colonists. A draftee, he was slightly older than the others, blond hair, mustache and glasses. His deep, gravelly voice seemed to transcend the awful jungle living conditions as he quoted self-scripted poetry. When Gambler received his draft notice, his wife divorced him as he prepared to ship out. In spite of this he was a good Marine and maintained a contagious optimism.

Gambler shared his foxhole with Rhonda, a plump-faced, "aw shucks" teenager from Georgia. Rhonda was named after a famous drag racer he idolized, Gas Rhonda. They had a mutual interest in building race cars, and they talked racing technology into the wee hours of the night. Scrawled on the camouflaged cover of his steel combat helmet was, "Little Green Machine," in dark letters.

Gambler was holding a fresh case of C-Rations held together by baling wire. Utilizing the three-pronged flash suppressor on his M-16 rifle as a wire cutter, he twisted the rifle until the sharp edges of the flash suppressor cut the wire.

"Perfect! Who's got a John Wayne?" He would have first choice of the selection of meals but needed a P-38 can opener named after the famous movie star.

"Here you go Gambler," yelled Blowfish, a round kid who seemed to puff up when he spoke. He tossed several John Wayne's to Gambler who had dug out his favorite meal, Beans and Franks or "Winnies." He tossed the fruit cake, cigarettes and the essential butt wipe to Blowfish.

Blowfish was a young politician in a small New Mexico town when he volunteered for the Marines before he received his draft notice. His infectious smile and his ability to expound on any subject earned his nick name, "Blowfish."

In the next hole was Gator, a tall, skinny Black Marine from Florida. Gator was reading the community paperback book, the only one available to the platoon. Gator was "short," short of time left in Vietnam and he kept a short timer's calendar to remind him of how many days he had left. He had spent twelve months living in the "bush," (living out in the elements of Mother Nature), and he was down to a matter of days.

"If I had as many days left as you, I would kill myself," he would chuckle to newcomer Hamster.

Gator's buddy, Atlas was a weightlifter from the Bronx. To these Marines skin color was not a uniform, what mattered was underneath. Black, Mexican, Asian, Puerto Rican or White, they were all "green" Marines supporting each other to the end. To some extent it was a working atmosphere of cooperation that Roberts had never experienced.

Roberts' machine gun crew was set up on the path running up Hill 555. The path was the most obvious avenue of approach since two sides of the hill were near cliffs but that did not preclude an attack from those areas. Every part of the perimeter had to be protected. Sweetness was the gunner; Carson was the A gunner or assistant gunner whose role was to direct fire, carry ammo (ammunition) and take over the gun if the gunner was a casualty. They were a pair, both hilarious in their own way and the best of friends.

Sweetness was an adventurer, joined the Marines after one year of college in Kentucky. His Mom would write him every day asking if he was OK and of course he suffered through lots of ribbing. He had a private pilot's license and they all encouraged him to try and get into flight school. He would quietly say, "maybe so but I love carrying the gun, this is my Baby." Then he would smile and plant a big kiss on the barrel whispering, "Get some Baby."

Carson, a Johnny Carson, (TV late night show host and comedian) look-alike, was from Mississippi, joined the Marines because his Dad was career Army. All he could talk about was how his girlfriend would not write him and she was probably with "Jodie," the name of all the guys at home who were dating all Marines' women. When the mail would arrive, he would yell, "Don't bring that stuff down here, I don't want to hear from her now." Then when all of the mail was handed out, he would sit, dejectedly, muttering obscenities.

The LP (Listening Post) was returning, faces covered with centipede stings and the look of utter exhaustion in their eyes. The LP was usually positioned out about 30 meters in front of their lines and down the trail to detect any surprise enemy activity. Gloria and Yacker, what a pair. Gloria was a draftee from Seattle who got his name because he looked like the Platoon Sergeant's girlfriend. He was married with two girls and got unfairly drafted when he dropped out of college and started a rock band. His notorious donkey laugh was silent as they walked through the lines and to their foxhole.

Yacker was a very quiet Hoosier, drafted right out of high school less than six months ago. In high school he had been a multisport athlete and his agility, stamina and strength were remarkable. He always set the standard for most everything they did, and it was a joke when someone would do something and remark in hostile humor, "Beat that Yacker!"

The platoon CP (command post) was behind Roberts' share of the Company line and was in the center about 10 meters from the platoon's perimeter. There radioman Bluto, Doc and the Lieutenant communicated, directed and looked after the welfare of the platoon.

Doc was busy handing out the weekly orange malaria pill. Orders required that he watch each Marine swallow the pill. Most Marines hid it under their tongue believing it would cause diarrhea, laughable since diarrhea was a chronic affliction of jungle life. Additionally, the Marines were required to take a small, white pill daily because the variant of malaria was different in the mountainous jungles than was encountered along the DMZ (Demilitarized Military Zone), their normal AO (Area of Operation.)

The Doc was interesting, a Jimmy Stewart (Hollywood actor) clone, he would conduct office visits in his deep Tennessee drawl. When he was drafted, he thought he could avoid Vietnam by volunteering for the Navy, not realizing that the Navy Medical Corps provided medical care for the Marines. After being goaded incessantly, the Lieutenant allowed Doc to teach him how to chew tobacco, a sorrowful episode and he would remember the disgusting taste for the rest of his life. Of course, it became platoon lore, the young Lieutenant nearly tossing his C-rations when he tried such an adult activity.

The radioman, Bluto, acquired his name from Popeyes's unshaven nemesis, Bluto. He became Roberts best friend, always there, teaching, supporting and advising. He seemed to never sleep, never complain and always had a know-it-all smile shining through his beard. It didn't matter how much he shaved; he could never get a clean shave in the jungle. Bluto spent a year traveling the country in a van until he got his draft notice and talked incessantly about home. His favorite phrase was, "When I get back to the World, I will be somebody," and "Where is my Freedom Bird?" The "World" was home and the "Freedom Bird" was the plane home.

As the sun rose, Roberts could see that Bluto was rereading a letter from the father of one of his friends, killed just a month ago. As most young Marines who see friends die, he blamed himself. "I should have told him that," Bluto would lament.

"It is a war son," his lost friend's Dad wrote to Bluto. "There was nothing you could have done." It made no difference; guilt washed his being.

To his left he could see his Platoon Sergeant called "Skier" because of his love for the sport. He was from Idaho and a mini-John Wayne, tough, smart and a professional Marine. He had gained his rocker (Staff Sergeant stripe) quickly and had orders to attend the prestigious Drill Instructor school but he had to survive another month of Vietnam. Skier and the Doc usually shared a foxhole, but the layout was better if Doc was close to the CP.

An interesting addition was Dung, the Vietnamese Kit Carson Scout. Dung was 22 and looked 12. His slight build and complete lack of muscle tone suggested he would be weak but that was a dangerous assumption. Dung was a former enemy Viet Cong guerrilla from the Hue area in the northeastern corner of South Vietnam. Dung had switched from the Communist side to support the Americans effort. Dung was part of the Company Commander's staff but preferred working with Robert's platoon. He especially liked Hamster, a BNG (Brand New Guy) who quickly picked up the nickname "Hamster Face" because of his mousey nose, round head and very short neck. Hamster was learning his survival skills from Turtle. If Hamster could survive for forty-five days, he had a good chance of making it home after a year.

Dung asked Beachboy if his hair could be blond like his. He thought women would love him because he would be so different and special compared to other black-haired Vietnamese men. The irony was that they were hundreds of kilometers from the nearest available women.

"My hair wook wike his?" he asked pointing to Beachboy. Doc, nodding "yes," provided a large bottle of peroxide and Beachboy poured the whole bottle over Dung's silky black hair.

Dung smiled an "I gonna' be so cool" smile as his hair began to change from a deep black to a deep red to a lighter red, then suddenly stopped changing. His hair was so thick and black it would not change from black to red to blonde. He looked into a mirror and smiled.

Next, he wanted his face shaved so Hamster got a razor and some soap. Although he didn't have a hair on his face Dung wanted to be shaved, nose, cheeks, forehead and all.

Later Dung asked if he could borrow Roberts K-Bar (Marine trench knife), then cut a 12-inch length of bamboo. As he worked on the bamboo, his face relaxed and he seemed to be the boy he had once been. When he was done, he handed the Lieutenant a hand carved flute.

"Give to son."

"He is a nice young man, one of us," the Lieutenant thought as he reflected on the contradiction. Just a few month ago, as enemies, they would have killed each other, now they were friends and allies proving that common ground between humans is always possible.

About mid-morning the Lieutenant heard rustling in the brush about twenty meters to his right. He knew another Marine Company was moving through their position but had no idea of who the surprise guest might be. Out stepped, or more appropriately stumbled, Tom McDonald or Mac, a friend from OCS and Basic School, the first person he met on his first day in the Marines. His blonde hair matted to his round, beet red face, his entire countenance bathed in sweat, he was beaming a huge smile. Struggling up the hillside he plopped down next to him and asked, "How's it going Lieutenant," a wry ear-to-ear smile covering his face.

Literally, the young Lieutenant was overcome with pride, both in Mac and in the Marine Corps. How fortunate he was to be associated with such wonderful young men! He was moved to the point of tears and he knew they both would do anything for each other. They had time to catch up with the rumors and news about their classmates in Vietnam. Soberly, they touched on many of whom had already been killed or wounded and sent home. Swenson was shot down in a helicopter, Cratchit paralyzed from a land mine, and Minelli killed in an ambush to name a few.

"How about some chow?" B-ration cans the size of large juice cans had arrived bringing hamburgers, his favorite craving. Laying a green, metal ammo box on its side, Roberts stuffed the inside with heat tablets creating a perfect grill. The paint peeled but they could care less. They were having real hamburgers, granted, a bit light green because of the paint on the ammo box, but a hamburger indeed. Mac magically produced ketchup and they both opened a can of C-Ration crackers instantly creating hamburgers. From his pack, Roberts pulled out a coveted can of warm Coke, a passenger for weeks. He popped the top and poured some into Mac's canteen cup.

"Short round." Someone screamed from the top of the hill and immediate terror took over as Roberts looked up and he saw everyone looking, staring up into the air, mouths wide open. The mortar men's eyes looked like volleyballs as they stared in horror at the short round, then at the two Lieutenants, friendly, unwelcome targets. The 60 mm round was barely 20 meters out of the mortar tube and already beginning its downward trip with them in the target zone. Roberts could read the writing on the side as it slowly twisted its' way up, then began to nosedive. This was the proverbial moment of truth.

The two friends both looked at their burgers, then at the rapidly approaching round. Tough choice but they dropped the hamburgers and Coke and jumped, then dove, down the side of the hill, rolling over logs and sticks together laughing. The round was a dud and it lay in the path inches from his dirty hamburger and now near empty Coke can. Mac lost his burger but by now they both were used to dirt, so Roberts dusted the burger off, gave half to Mac and thanked God again, this time for the great burger.

Soon Mac moved on, disappearing into the darkness as quickly as he had appeared. Again, Roberts was overcome with unabashed pride, pride to be associated with such great people in a great organization. It motivated him to seek excellence and to give, expecting no return. It would be the last time he would ever see Mac.

As Mac and his Marines disappeared, Roberts saw a CH-46 Sea Knight helicopter drop low, then quickly rise in the distant jungle. Under it dangled a long rope with objects swinging with the sway of the chopper. The dark green machine was a work horse for the Marines bringing supplies, ferrying troops and extracting Marines in stress. Machine gun fire chased it upwards and green enemy tracers forked around its body. Two OV-10A Broncos, an O-1 Bird Dog AO (aerial observer), hovered overhead, made several rocket-passes but were virtually helpless to assist the plodding chopper.

As it got closer, he could see that people were hanging from the long rope ladder, limp sagging backwards, their heads tossing with the wind. It circled the Landing Zone (LZ) several times, and then dropped down, hovering as the Marines wilted to the ground. Their faces were painted camouflage green, their heads wrapped in camouflaged scarves like do-rags. They were Recons or Reconnaissance Marines who go out in teams of four, six or nine to gather intelligence about the enemy.

Roberts hurried over and helped unhook their snap links and gently laid them on the ground calling for a Corpsman. They were alive but in bad shape. Two had head wounds, one had a serious body wound.

The leader, a Corporal, was very thankful for the assistance and for taking care of his Marines. They had barely escaped capture or death. Giving Roberts his snap link, he said it was all he had to thank him. It was enough just to be there to help, Roberts thought.

"Lieutenant, two of my Marines, I couldn't get them back, we have to go back and get them." He was desperate and it was unnecessary for him to acknowledge the unsaid obvious, they were both dead, but that did not change the urgency of the mission, Marines never abandon their comrades, dead or alive, regardless of how dangerous the mission. It is a fundamental way of valuing each other; you are important enough for me to risk my own life to find you, because I know you would do the same for me. The Corporal was responsible for his men and he was going to get them home because they had already willingly given their lives for their comrades.

The NVA, or Charley as the Marines called them, had chased this team for several days nearly putting an end to their patrol when fortunately, the chopper plucked them out to safety. Two of them didn't make the chopper.

"We've got to go back and get my guys!" Energy and determination filled his young face, eyes squinting into the long shadows of the mountains. "Sir, we gotta go now!"

There was no blame in his face, only responsibility, there was no shaming each other, only pride and support and no explaining what happened. Explaining was only making excuses for what happened, and none was required. But the urgency was real, the jungle quickly reclaims everything.

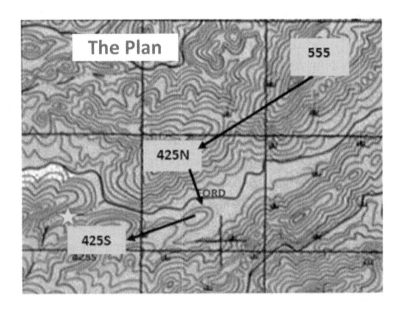

Chapter 2

The Patrol

It didn't take long to get approval. Quickly they went to work planning the recovery patrol, then reviewing the details with Roberts' platoon. They discussed what they might find and how they would react. This would be different than any mission they had been on before because they would operate it like a raid, something that seldom happened for regular line companies. As the training session wore on, they all posed every possible situation they could imagine. Roberts set the objectives and parameters, but they negotiated the details. Many of his Marines had been in Vietnam longer than he had been a Marine. Sometimes experience counted more than rank, but people had to earn the right to negotiate.

They had to recover those Marines, had to. The plan was to move 3 kilometers (about two miles) west down Hill 555, across a river and back up another hill to reclaim two dead Recon Marines. He would have no problem gaining support from his platoon.

At this point the strength of the platoon was twenty-eight Marines and Doc, the Navy Corpsman, about half the Table of Organization. Attrition was swift in this infernal jungle and replacements were slow, now largely fueled by the Draft.

The Company Commander offered up Dung, the Kit Carson Scout and Triggerman, the engineer. As Dung was a former enemy Viet Cong guerrilla, he had excellent jungle sense and worked well as a translator. He would be a great asset on this dangerous mission. Roberts turned down the scout dog and sniper.

Triggerman was a stocky Black Marine from Virginia who was an artisan with explosives. He once told Roberts in confidence that he had never been around any white people before and this was an enlightening experience. Roberts conceded that this was an enlightening experience for them all.

In his mind the Lieutenant continually reviewed the Marine Corps Five Paragraph Order known as "SMEAC," and a college leadership program that encapsulated his responsibilities. "PLOC, Plan, Lead, Organize and Control." Within those responsibilities he would explain SMEAC, the enemy Situation as he understood it, the Mission of reclaiming their dead Marine comrades, how they would organize the Execution of the mission, what Administrative and Logistics support they could expect and how they would organize the Command structure and most importantly, the communications. All the maps were marked with the current reference thrust points at the intersection of certain grid lines. He marked "fruits," "cars," "beer," and "girl's names," as they were in their AO (Area of Operation).

The platoon would establish an ORP (Organizational Rally Point) as soon as they reached the location of the fallen Recons. Then Doc, the Recon Corporal along with six Marines, would make their way from the perimeter of the ORP and form a security perimeter around the site of the fallen Marines while Hogan and Doc identified and bagged the bodies. Then the six would carry the body bags to the rally point and they would coordinate the pickup with a prearranged chopper.

The Lieutenant was planning on a three-day mission but prepared for four days' worth of C-rations, Long-Rats (Freeze-dried long-range patrol rations) and plenty of water. Because of the constant rain, he could not depend upon any resupply. Twice in the last two months they had resorted to scavenging food in the jungle for survival when the severe rain and fog grounded the supply helicopters.

Each radioman had extra Papa Sierras (power supplies), command frequencies and call names. In the jungle covered mountains the power supplies never lasted long because of the heat, humidity and terrain so the range of the PRC-25 was spotty at best. Sometimes for some inexplicable reason, they just had no range and Roberts wondered if the humidity was responsible. But they couldn't accomplish their mission without the radios. Everyone would carry a LAW rocket launcher, claymore mines, trip flares and a can of machine gun ammo bringing each individual carrying a load close to 75 lbs.

Each Marine had four sticks of C4 explosives, and Roberts pressed hard on his Marines to not use it for cooking, it was for demolition. They had a visual location of the extraction point and artillery coordinates, so from that data they determined the most likely location on the map.

In preparation for the patrol, Roberts had Zoo, the Company armorer, go through the M-60 machine gun. He didn't want any problems like they had in the past. The receivers cracked and the guns jammed after one shot. Zoo reported that Roberts' gun was also cracked, useless as an automatic weapon.

After discussions with the Company Commander and the Weapons Platoon Commander, Roberts made his way to the artillery battery's position on the top of Hill 555 to visit Captain Grog, the battery commander. He would not leave without Captain Grog's machine gun.

"What if we need it?" the Captain was going to be difficult but that didn't stop Roberts. How many times did the artillery need a machine gun, Roberts thought? The blond Captain developed a stern, obstinate mask. Weak argument Roberts thought.

"With all due respect Captain, the only way you would need that gun would be because ours won't work. If you remember, we are your security."

After a minute of obligatory consideration, he nodded. "Make sure it's clean when you bring it back Lieutenant."

"Yessir!"

Zoo checked out the machine gun from the artillery battery and muttered, "This gun is brand new. Why do they get a fresh gun?"

The Recon leader was called "Hogan," after the famous golfer Ben Hogan, his hometown hero. He would provide on-the-ground guidance as they headed west, downhill from the Company Command Post on Hill 555.

Their path would go southwest 1,500 meters or what was referred to as a "click and a half," to Hill 425N. (A "click" is short for kilometer, 1,000 meters or about 610 yards.) From there they would go south, cross a river and set up the ORP on Hill 425S, close to the extraction point. The dead Marines would be within 200 meters of that location. Once they identified the bodies, they would take them back to the extraction point and have them evacuated.

Hogan was a 19-year-old Corporal from Texas, and very confident as he advised what equipment they should take, then briefed them on the terrain. The triple canopied jungle would require a jungle penetrator for extraction of the bodies and would prohibit their boarding of the helicopter. The penetrator had two folded seats and appeared like a giant, weighted treble fishing hook attached to the rescue line that was winched from the helicopter. It was the only thing that could push through the extraordinary cover, cover so dense it blocked out most of the daylight.

The radioman Bluto, Hogan, Skier and the Lieutenant met with the Company FO (artillery Forward Observer) and registered prearranged artillery coordinates. He asked if they wanted his

Alpha (Alpha for Assistant FO) to accompany them but Hogan politely interrupted.

"I can handle the arty and air, Sir!" His blue eyes shined with certainty.

The terrain was tricky. Where the river cut between Hill 425N and 425S there were steep cliffs making the trajectory of the support artillery a difficult target. They would have to rely on the air cover, not a problem if they could keep the planes on station and the Monsoon rains and low ceiling did not keep the birds roosted.

"Song Chet," muttered Dung as he looked at the map, his forehead wrinkled; his eyes looked like huge black rocks as his lips grew quiet. He had been in this valley before, he motioned. "Dong Song Chet, Vietnamese call River of Death."

A chill shook Roberts shoulders as he moved on with the plans. The young Lieutenant did not want to know more.

The FAC (Battalion Forward Air Control Officer) had already scheduled an A-1 Skyhawk and an OV-10A Bronco to be on station for air support and evacuation helicopters were on full alert. The young Lieutenant learned early in his military career that you cannot over plan, there is always something that is left out, but he felt they were in the best possible shape to move out. As his Dad would say, failure happens in small missteps, not abruptly.

Despite all of this, through ingenuity they would always improvise to make things work wherever they went. They grew and learned to be the best of America, wonderfully talented, dedicated young men who knew that their past best was never good enough for completing the next hurdle. Each new obstacle stretched their confidence and built a deep pride in each other's accomplishments. Their fates were intertwined, their enduring trust unshakable.

Jungle dusk and night comes quickly, and the urgency would have to wait until early morning, the enemy owned the night trails. The Marines would set out ambushes or "Blackjacks" nightly, but seldom did they send out patrols at night, it was a certain path to death from a hidden ambush by the crafty enemy.

Before sunrise the next morning, word went through the Company that they were leaving the perimeter. Roberts made a final check of each Marine's equipment, checking their ammo and gear searching for any noise makers. Marines were notorious for hanging equipment that sounded like a Mariachi Band in the jungle and the distinctive sound carried a long way.

Sounds and smells, the essence of safety in the night cloaked jungle. Since none of the Marines had a chance to bath in weeks, their bodies had reached an odorless equilibrium, but Roberts and the other Marines had learned to sort out the smells of nature and the sickening smell of Charley.

Predictably, Pig Pen had his air mattress packed into a tight roll. "It took me months to get this baby so where I go, she goes."

So, with the plan in place, they saddled up and headed down the drenched jungle trail to recover their dead comrades, comrades they had never met, brothers who shared a common bond of pride and common purpose. It never crossed their minds for a single moment that they would fail. As a team, they knew that failure does not just happen, and he was amazed at how these kids became masters of details and "what ifs."

There was no sun yet to burn off the heavy mist and it felt like rain might be moving in. The air sucked into Roberts' mouth like a dense fog as the jungle wrapped its wicked arms around his chest and the stench of rotting jungle filled his nose. Their assault packs were light with supplies, but everyone carried a box of machine gun ammo, extra M16 bandoliers and three PRC-25 radios. Roberts had made the very unpopular decision the night before that everyone would wear a helmet and flak jacket, something that these kinds of operations sometimes left behind because of heat, weight and noise in the hot, humid, hostile jungle conditions. Marines always dug fox holes and wore flak jackets.

With Turtle at point and Hamster scurrying behind, they stepped into the jungle trail. Turtle was followed by a fireteam of Gambler, Marbles, Gloria, and Atlas. Next would be Hogan, Dung, the Lieutenant and radioman Bluto. Sweetness and Carson would follow with the machine gun. Doc and the rest of the platoon would be led by Skier. Yacker, Gator and Rhonda would provide rear security. With Hamster as his understudy, Turtle walked point like a beagle, no noise and an uncanny aptitude for discovering booby traps and ambushes along a trail. Turtle's preferred weapon walking point was a 12-gauge trench shot gun.

He was one of five Spanish speaking Marines, three from Mexico, and two from Puerto Rico, all excellent Marines. It was fun to watch them joke with each other in Spanish, using their own code of support. When one would get a package from home it was a "Mexican Holiday."

The only way to move in the jungle is over well-traveled trails, so dense and overgrown in spots that it almost masked the elevation. The Lieutenant was in great shape but sometimes going uphill was measured by how much he panted. The enemy knew these trails much better than anyone, the Ho Chi Minh Trail was a major part of their logistics system. It also was their home.

No words passed, only hand signals communicated the situation as they quietly crept downhill. Marines called this "humping" and the word worked as a noun and verb. Turtle raised his hand and pointed up into a tree revealing two sticks bound together into an arrow, a common "road sign" for the NVA.

Normally they would investigate but today their mission was to make it to their dead Marines and get them home. Bruno reported it to the Company. Casualty communication back to the World was quick and by now their relatives knew they were missing, and they had to bring closure for them.

The terrain was rugged, dense jungle covering steep mountains. Their path would start at Hill 555, 555 meters above sea level. The hill was on the eastern section of a lazy J, surrounded on all 4 sides by rivers and streams. It was approximately 4 kilometers north to south and 6 kilometers wide from east to west.

Hills 425N and 425S were on each side of the southern river. Their first objective was to scale and secure Hill 425N and dig in for the night. They would head down a steep slope in a southwest direction, the elevation dropping to 300 meters over the first 750 meters, a steep slope on a slick, muddy trail. Going downhill was just as tough as going uphill, heavy weapons and equipment hung at different angles and there was always the risk of slipping backwards onto one's back and landing on their e-tool.

A river ran northeast to southwest about 800 meters south and 150 meters below hill 555, then turned due west toward their objective. It would have been easy to take the riverbank to the objective, but it was too risky, the cliffs on both sides of the river gave the enemy the high ground all the way to the objective, too many convenient spots for ambushes and mortar attacks. They would hump the hills and take their chances in the jungle; its cover leveled the playing field. But they knew they would eventually have to cross the foreboding river.

The trail was damp with morning dew making the vines and tree roots slippery like an ice rink, between the roots the trail had a glaze of mud that clung to Roberts' boots, encasing the dog tag that he had laced to his boot. This was in addition to the tag on the chain around his neck and its purpose was to identify both halves of the casualty. On his helmet was his medevac number.

Leaves of ancient trees and bushes slapped his face as dots of sunlight peeked in under his helmet and mosquitos swarmed over his bare skin. Ominously, there were no sounds, odd for the morning, usually there were jungle sounds but now the only sound was their boots sucking in the gelatinous layer of mud and the sounds of shifting equipment and silent curses.

"Spread out," Roberts signaled with his left hand, the right clutching the handle of his M16 rifle. Small tennis shoe prints went both directions on the path as if someone was trying to connect the dots of locations. Along the way were tracks from bicycles that were used to quietly transport supplies. It was impossible to see the sunrise, but it didn't matter, the heat was a dead giveaway and the humidity didn't waste any time making it sorrier.

Roberts unconsciously scratched his belly, the heat rash from his flak jacket was a permanent and unwelcome guest, a gift from Mother Nature. As they quietly they slogged along he reflected on how proud he was of his kids, real professionals, teenagers, their childhood now gone forever in this dismal jungle.

Turtle and the point element disappeared as the trail dipped down, then up like a roller-coaster and then down around a bend. A small stream gurgled along next to them as it made its way down to the river. Without any warning, a fully automatic AK-47 NVA rifle broke the silence like an angry junk yard dog. Then, joined by several others, they ramped up to a deafening orchestra of solid sound, the trees cracking as the enemy bullets tore into the embankment behind them.

Like a race car revving up its engine, Hell had erupted, and they were instantly in a fight for their lives. They were in a "U" shaped ambush, green tracers coming at them from a semi-circle of NVA soldiers. The Marines dove off the trail and began to immediately return fire, automatic weapons raking the trail area as they vaulted off the path and into the jungle. A frag (fragmentation grenade) ripped through the trees, adrenaline pumped the young Lieutenant into a machine as he assessed the unfolding fight for survival. Bullets ripped through an ammo box; fragments stuck into his flak jacket, the noise was constant, unrelenting, deafening to the point of pain.

Immediate Action drills, survival training had taught him what to do without thinking, take "Immediate Action." Without thinking, his mind immediately assessed the situation, broke it down into problems and quickly implemented solutions to them as primal fear threatened to consume his heart.

Time stood still no future no past, only the present.; everything was in slow motion in a blurred flurry of movement. Combat was the ultimate stimulation, exhilarating, testing. Slowly blessed adrenaline replaced the fear, there was a larger need than his life. With bullets cracking over his head, fear tightened its debilitating grip around his throat, his body began to shake as he belly-crawled forward, unconsciously filling his open mouth with rotting jungle plants and insects. He was screaming at the top of his lungs but who could hear, a trickle of blood ran into his eye, then on his lips, a scratch. Would he ever get used to this?

The Lieutenant needed to immediately determine the size and location of the enemy and get superior fire laid on the ambush. He also knew he needed to protect their flanks and rear. Those were the immediate problems. As Skier directed fire from the platoon, Roberts quickly called up the machine gun.

"Guns up," he screamed as Sweetness and Carson braved the fire, setting their gun to the front of the column and its staccato voice brought a certain amount of comfort knowing they were fighting back. As soon as it began dealing out its own death pills, the firefight stopped as suddenly as it had started, at least over for now, so Roberts called cease fire. But just because it was quiet did not mean it was over.

"Corpsman up! Corpsman for God's sake, Doc!" His stomach churned, who had been hit and how bad was it? He moved the gun up for cover and made sure their flanks and rear were secured with a hasty perimeter. Their next set of problems would be how would they get the wounded onto a helicopter in the middle of a triple canopy jungle ceiling?

"Get a medevac on the line," he barked to Bluto, "and look for a place for an evacuation." Hogan immediately took the radio handset to call for an emergency Medevac (medical evacuation.) He knew the area well and didn't need any encouragement to scout out an area where a chopper could come in for an extraction.

"This is what I do, may I take it, Sir?" The Lieutenant nodded as he and Doc crawled toward the bend, gun in place and with a fireteam of Marines covering the beaten zone of the ambush. Four Marines, his kids, lay face down, rifles still in their hands. Hamster was applying a tourniquet and appeared to have only minor wounds, but he wasn't so optimistic about the others.

"Rake the area beyond them with covering fire and make sure they are not still waiting for us, put a blooper in there," he directed Sweetness and his machine gun and the M-79 grenade launcher. It was not uncommon for the enemy to draw them into another ambush as Marines reclaimed their casualties, so he wasn't about to take any chances. Burps of lead ripped into the ambush site until he was convinced, at least guardedly convinced, that they could get to the injured and treat their wounds.

He and Doc crawled quickly like snakes down the trail to the two Marines, both still alive but badly wounded. Marbles' eyes bulged, blood ran down his lips and onto his chin. He had a large, smoking hole in his flak jacket. Gambler was motionless, quiet, his helmet lay next to him, blond hair gently lay across his forehead. Discipline and training told him "A, B, C, Airways, Bleeding and

Shock," the drill went through his mind as they worked on his Marines.

Doc was like a magician pulling rabbits from a hat. Out came compressions bandages for each of them as they cleared their airways so they could breath and staunched the flow of blood. Once they could breath and the blood flow slowed, Doc shot them both with morphine, a blessing in the battlefield but a curse later. Pig Pen quickly moved up with his fireteam and the Lieutenant sent them out ahead to make sure the area was clear, no enemy, they had said their piece and disappeared into the heavy, opaque, vegetation. A withdrawal of only a few meters and the jungle would swallow them up, invisible. Don't relax your guard, he thought.

The two other Marines were also seriously hit, and they needed to be evacuated pronto. Blowfish's leg hung by a thread, Hamster's tourniquet staunching the blood flow; face contorted as he held in the pain. Nester was knocked cold by a round that went through his helmet, the other a gut wound. Doc injected them both with morphine and prepared the evacuation information cards.

"Bird is on the way and it can get a jungle penetrator into an area about 100 meters up hill," Hogan whispered! Good news for sure so they slipped the wounded Marines onto ponchos and, after he dispersed a securing perimeter at the evacuation location, they carried the casualties to the site. Mercifully, the morphine choked out the pain. Gambler shook, grew slack and his young face looked peaceful as it took on a pale, stone-look, his life seemed on the brink of abandoning his bullet riddled body.

"Hang on Gambler, hang on buddy, you are just going to be fine and back in the world before you know it!" Doc had a great bedside manner, he believed he could save anyone and convince them that they had to live. "I will kick your Yankee ass if you let go." Whatever it takes, do it.

"Sir, they are gone," Doc whispered, "Gambler and Marbles, I couldn't save them."

Doc appeared on the brink of tears as Roberts put his hand on Doc's and muttered, "You can't reverse destiny, they were too far gone, you did your best." Navy Corpsmen thought they could save anyone, but the reality was they were in a jungle, miles from traumatic medical assistance and to say their resources were limited was an overstatement. They were wonderful young men.

As they made their way toward the extraction location, out popped an NVA with no weapon, hands up, crying, "Chieu Hoi, Chieu Hoi!" Pronounced, "Chew Hoy," it was a program that allowed the enemy to give themselves up, defection would be another term for it. He looked like he had been out there a long time, uniform ragged and his face drawn from stress and poor nutrition.

Now Roberts had a prisoner but what was he going to do with a prisoner? Maybe use him for intelligence and a guide to work with Hogan? It would be to the enemy's advantage to steer clear of his buddies, they weren't very fond of Chieu Hoi turncoats.

"Frisk the bastard," he told Beachboy, a short blonde headed kid from California, "and make sure he is unarmed and tie his hands behind his back. Hogan, tell the bird they have a prisoner and see if they can take him back."

"Sir, they can't take the prisoner, they are full but can return later. What should I tell them, Sir?" Roberts didn't have time to wait but he didn't want to cut his tie to them.

"We will have them take the prisoner when they pick up the aces." Aces were code for dead Marines and to the choppers a low priority "routine" pickup.

"Beachboy, you and Dung, are responsible to make sure he behaves, if he gets out of line shoot him." Beachboy knew enough

Vietnamese to get his point across, the prisoner nodded in panicked agreement. Dung uttered an ominous threat in Vietnamese. The prisoner spoke some English, curious for an NVA Snuffy. As he nodded, the Lieutenant heard the CH-46 overhead.

Helicopters, especially the larger birds, announced their arrival way in advance, sometimes to their own detriment. As the whapping of the rotor blades grew louder, the trees began to whisper its approach, rustling, then waving as though signaling their locations. Hogan was an expert, guiding the craft overhead, no smoke to give away their positions before the bird arrived.

Hovering, he could see the small crane and the crew chief looking out of the door. It looked like the jungle penetrator was caught on limbs but broke through and lowered to the ground. Both Marines were alive but unconscious, so Doc tied the first one in place with the harness and signaled the crew chief to lift them up. As the lift began to rise Doc's wedding ring became entangled in the sling and he was lifted off the ground, face in an agonizing grimace. Hogan quickly jumped under Doc's feet and lifted him up freeing his nearly severed finger.

"'It's all right, that's what's important," as he watched Blowfish slowly disappear, his war done. The empty basket dropped back down, and Nester followed Blowfish home. Then, mercifully, the chopper crew asked for the Aces and the poncho wrapped bodies of Gambler and Marbles left the jungle and headed home. The extraction went without further incident.

Everyone opened a can of C-rations and gobbled down the contents before they headed back uphill. They were back on the trail before noon, headed for the dead Reconnaissance Marines.

His Marines were shaken so Roberts circulated among them, encouraging, demanding attention to the tasks and security of the patrol. The sun was now almost overhead, and the sweat squirted out of their skin like miniature fountains. Drinking water would be a problem if they got delayed much more but there was always rain and river water.

Where to place the POW in their patrol? He had a presence that he had not seen in other prisoners. Had he given himself up or was he in the wrong place at the wrong time? He placed him between the guns and Dung with Beachboy close by. That way Roberts could also keep track of him, he didn't trust the NVA prisoner as far as he could throw him, but he couldn't do what everyone really wanted to do, shoot him. Since he was now coming along, Roberts thought he might come in handy if he senses an ambush and tried to bolt. It was something he thought likely and the main reason he put him up front.

The prisoner was affectionately nicknamed "Luke the Puke" by the Marines and the Lieutenant turned him over to Beachboy and Dung the scout. If Luke made any move Dung would handle it, his way. Roberts learned early that leaders set the standards for behavior and understood how quickly bad behavior could become the standard. Condoning the wrong behavior was a slippery slope to lawless mayhem and destruction.

Pig Pen took over the point position and Turtle dropped back in the next fireteam. Walking point was always stressful, especially when enemy contact is made, and it was a necessity to rotate the responsibility. Two other Marines took over the point fireteam position and they moved ahead, sweat pouring saturating their camo trousers and green T-shirts, leeches clinging to their legs, but there were no complaints. It was their job, very simple.

As night fell, the platoon formed a perimeter around the top of the night's objective, Hill 425N. The darkness was suffocating, bringing out the jungle life like creepy crawlers, the day's heat replaced by a chill. The Marines dug foxholes and set up night watches after placing trip flares and Claymore mines around the perimeter. Gramps, the old man at twenty-two was a former college linebacker, and Ozark, a draftee from Missouri, were the LP's.

The slight drizzle turned the dark into a wet blanket as the Lieutenant and his trusted radioman, Bluto, dug their chest deep hole through heavy roots and rocks. Roberts learned early, share the risks, share the work and keep the spirits up.

Jungle nights were surreal conjuring up nightmares of vampires, zombies and werewolves. The jungles were full of real-life versions and the sounds of the night jungle were cavernous. The silence deafening, thick with nothingness except death dragging a person down, one note at a time.

The jungle is a constant struggle of survival, a life and death adventure for all live organisms, each trying to gain advantage over their prey. Every animal has its own voice, talking, warning, and complaining. Even plants had voices at night, whispering creaks and groans. It is an environment based solely on survival, every organism competing for space, air, food and water for existence. For a human it is a constant war of survival and every single second in the jungle is consumed with defending against man-eating wild animals, surrealistic insects, poisonous snakes, itchy plants and unpredictable atmospheric conditions. Every tiny time measurement is survival of the fittest and everything must adapt to the point that it becomes real life. Roberts forgot the amenities of civilization; he was completely consumed in the primitive activities of jungle survival.

"Sir, did you know that there are abdominal snowmen in this area," whispered Bluto? Roberts just shook his head in disbelief.

Almost on que, the hoot bird started its dove imitation and Roberts had to smile. Nobody ever saw the hoot bird and it always sounded like the very same bird, following them and standing watch in the trees. Undisturbed, it would hoot and toot but clammed up if there were any abnormal noises, a "watch bird."

Soon the radio crackled clicking three times, the LP's signal that there was movement by their position outside the lines. Roberts crawled up to the perimeter and slipped into the closest foxhole with Turtle and BNG Hamster, listening to the rustling brush. There was a low, barely audible low, deep breathing. In front of him less than five meters out was a huge tiger prowling toward them. How can they scare it off and not give away their position?

Without thinking, Hamster stood up and threw a C-ration can of beans and franks, hitting the tiger squarely on the nose. Startled, it hesitated, let out a loud roar and disappeared into the murky trees and vines, looking for something less threatening to chomp on.

The young Lieutenant sat in the hole with his Marines for a few minutes, smiling, happy that a can of beans and franks had saved them but then wondered why he didn't use the universally disliked ham and limas? Nobody ate those but after all, Hamster was a BNG and he would learn soon enough the value of things.

At dawn they began to move again. The morning brought the usual jungle maladies. Mosquitoes had feasted on everyone's lips and faces; arms and wrists were swollen from large centipede stings. Business as usual in the jungle, but there were only jokes, no complaints. The tiger took the creep award for the night.

Before he signaled Turtle to move out, Roberts told Hogan to call in their new plan. It was imperative to keep all the units informed, especially their artillery and air support. There were no other units close by, but they all needed to know the platoon's position.

They were making good time now and he hoped to be at the night's objective by late afternoon. As they descended a sharp decline, Turtle, back on point, raised his hand and signaled for Roberts to move up. As he passed the POW, he could smell the jungle stench and hate as he slipped by Luke, holding his temper and impulses. Nobody would have ever criticized him for doing what his instincts told him to do but that would be against his personal and professional code and set a bad precedence for the future of his command. But there was something about Luke, not sure what. He wasn't the run of the mill NVA.

Turtle had come to a man-made clearing approximately 30 meters wide and there appeared to be a small but deep, fast stream running through it. It smacked of a field of fire that was cut along the stream, an obstacle that would slow them down and make them perfect targets for the NVA. The path ran directly into the clearing and across the stream, then turned left and on up another hill. He decided to turn left off of the trail and make their way through the thick jungle vegetation with dense fern ground cover. It was a very difficult maneuver, but it would be an unanticipated move to the enemy who obviously expected them to follow the trail.

Turtle was cursing quietly in Spanish as he tried to pick a path of least resistance and stay hidden from the clearing. Within 30 minutes they had reached the southernmost tip of the hazardous clearing. As they turned west to circumvent the tip, the stream at this point had unexpectedly expanded into more of an obstacle. Stream crossings were the ultimate in vulnerability and more time was lost preparing for crossing it.

"We see that all of the time Lieutenant, maps in this area suck. They were made from radar imaging, I go by compass and feel," Hogan muttered as they lay in the mud listening to the deceivingly peaceful gurgle of the blue-gray water.

What now, Roberts thought, and quickly put together a plan, called Skier and his three squad leaders, Red, Thorny and Judy, together and issued his orders. Judy's first squad had two fireteams and he assigned them along with the machine gun team to cover the fireteam crossing the stream. Red's second squad would send a fireteam across the stream while Thorny's third squad would provide perimeter security.

As the Lieutenant lay watching the plan unfold, leaches squirmed out of the mud and onto his face. They epitomized the jungle at its worst, always there, always sucking blood. The triple canopied jungle shut down the light making his men virtually invisible to the eye. Damn he loved these kids, teenagers caught up in an unpopular war in a horrible place. A year ago, they were in high school. His main job was to take care of them and inspire them to do things they never thought possible, always doing what the situation demanded, no excuses, just do it.

The covering squad spread out along the stream; the gun stayed in between the covering squad and Roberts. As the three Marines crossed the swiftly moving stream, loose equipment that had not been secured was quickly swept downstream or sunk to the bottom. Slime covered stones offered no sure footing and each Marine took turns slipping to their knees bringing the water neck-deep, soaking everything. Gramps slipped on a rock and submerged to his helmet. On they went, slogging into an unknown danger, legs useless if the enemy decided to strike.

Turtle, Hamster and Skier struggled out of the stream and quickly moved to secure the left flank, the second team mirrored that, but moving right. After a brief security sweep, they signaled the all clear and the second fireteam along with Hogan and the POW, Luke, moved across to set up a new perimeter.

The same process followed up to the last fireteam, Roberts crossed with their rear protection. The water was chilling, clear and much stronger than he had imagined, the flow pushing at his boots, fingers of water under the soles, dragging them downstream. What he could not see from the bank was what was in the stream as it flowed by. In with the vegetation were large, winged insects looking for a meal and several snakes slithering around his boots.

In several spots he saw evidence that the enemy had crossed at the same point. Uniform parts, a weapon and some ammo lay at the bottom of the stream along with what looked like a mortar round and a bicycle wheel.

The last man was out of the stream and the squad leaders formed up, heading back north to meet up with the trail. They were on their way again and getting very close to their night objective, Hill 425S. Somewhere to the west he could hear the Skyhawk patrolling. Roberts always felt like he was a participant in the early aviation days of WWI when he heard the deep, powerful radial engine, it was frightening as well as comforting.

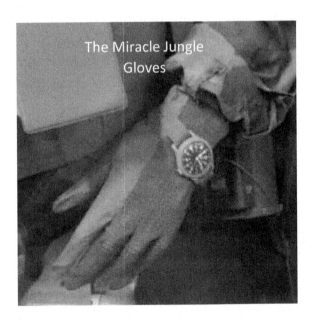

The Miracle Jungle Gloves

Chapter 3

HILL 425 NORTH

Hill 425N was an ass-kicker after the stream crossing, so Lieutenant Roberts called a short halt to check in by radio and verify their coordinates. He and Hogan agreed, they were right where they expected to be but about two hours late.

"Turtle wants the Lieutenant up front," so Roberts low crawled slowly to the point to talk to him.

"What's up Turtle," Roberts whispered. Turtle pointed to a cave entrance that was covered with fresh footprints.

"Some kinda supply point looks like to me. Should we go in, check it out?" His Spanish-accented voice was barely audible, lips mouthing each syllable.

"Wait one, I need to check with the CO." Having such a large enemy position behind him did not feel right and his inclination was to go in, investigate, neutralize any enemy and mark it for demolition later.

Check it out and report. Watch out for booby traps! It was a small, concealed opening to what resembled a cave reinforced with logs. Pig Pen led his fireteam in first to investigate. After dropping their packs, in they went, defeating their own fears of the unknown and nothingness. Soon they reappeared, almost smiling.

"Looks like a hospital Lieutenant, full of medical gear and cots. No enemy, but not abandoned. They were here earlier in the day. Some women's clothing, some weapons, come in and look around." Pig Pen smirked as he tossed some women under clothing onto the ground.

Crouching down until his knees were close to the dirt, Roberts took in the scene. Remarkable! How long did it take to stage all this gear? The NVA were logistic experts at seeding the battlefield with hidden equipment, ready for the next offensive. Where were the other entrances and where were the personnel?

The enemy had just left, pots boiling, and women's clothing drying on clotheslines. Camouflaged next to the entrance was a large 10-foot by 10-foot storage bin full of freshly harvested, unpolished rice. Before he could speak some of the Marines were digging through the rice with their hands looking for weapons and souvenirs.

"Trip wire," someone warned, another Marine screamed, "Snake, snake," as a bamboo pit viper struck out! By the time the slack was pulled out of the trip wire and the pin pulled from the clandestine grenade, everyone was clear. The explosion blew rice and debris into the trees and onto their backs.

"Skier, pass the word, no souvenir scrounging without my approval." This was probably a rice cache stolen from the farmers along the river. It took a colossal effort to move it bag by bag but where were they? Luke, the POW, had to tell us, he knew. Roberts was boiling inside, anger clawing its way to take control.

"Get Luke in here!" In came Luke, hands bound, Dung's rifle barrel buried in his back.

"Where everybody," Dung demanded! Fear bent Luke's face into a tan prune.

"Di Di," he mumbled, arms pulling against the det-cord (detonation cord used for arming C-4). around his wrists. His head pointed around in a circle, all around them he was saying. It did make sense from what they had seen so far but he knew he had an objective of self-preservation.

"Bluto get the old man on the net. Need to find out what he wants to do." They had enough C4 explosives to cause major damage, but he didn't want to use it in case they needed to use it for emergency medevacs.

"Captain, what do you want us to do with this hospital, Sir? I think we need to blow it, but I don't have the time nor the resources to do much damage. I think we should put some air and artillery on it after we depart, do you copy, over?"

He listened carefully to his orders, and the CO agreed with his plan. They would mark the spot, call in the coordinates, and when their mission was finished, they would call in airstrikes and blow it to Hell. But what he was not comfortable with, was the fact that there were still a large number of NVA in the area that they had not pinpointed, so as he mulled over the plan. He decided it might be better to call in airstrikes as soon as they left this position.

"Bluto, get the Old Man on the line again."

"Sir, I think we should blow this place with air and artillery as soon as we leave this position, if we don't, we're leaving our rear vulnerable to attack and supplying the resources for them to do it. Do you copy over?"

Again, he listened carefully to the CO's orders. The Captain agreed, need to blow this thing as soon as possible, they cannot leave this kind of fortification and logistical resource for the enemy one minute longer.

"Roger out." Roberts handed the handset back to Bluto.

"Hogan, get the Skyhawk on the map and have him mark this spot so they can obliterate it when we are a safe distance in the morning."

"Roger that Lieutenant, we may have to settle for an AO in a Bronco but that's just as good. He can coordinate them both."

They were in for the night now. He had the squads dispersed around the military crest of the hill as Ozark and Gramps headed out to the listening posts. Prompted by the sunset, jungle animals and insects again merged in a harmonic symphony. 50% awake 50% asleep, all night long with his squad leaders, the Platoon Sergeant Skier and the Lieutenant checking the lines all night. They set out the claymores and trip flares, but he knew soon they would hear some movement, he could feel it.

"Papa two, Papa Two, if you're all secure click two times!" Bluto was making his hourly radio check with the listening post. Two static bursts came through the handset, all secure.

"Hogan, let's take a look at the map, register artillery on some of these coordinates around our perimeter." Along with Skier, they slipped under a poncho, turned on the red flashlight, carefully looking through the terrain surrounding hill 425N. Roberts thought, if I were the enemy what avenue of approach would I use? How can I probe my lines to take advantage of my position and vulnerabilities? The most likely avenue of approach was from the Southwest through a gorge allowing the enemy protection on their flanks but not from the front, so he set the machine gun's principle direction of fire along with a fireteam to protect that approach.

Another interesting aspect of Hill 425N was that it plateaued off to the northwest leaving an open field of fire and a hill that did not show up on the map posed an interesting vulnerability as it rose to their west. Line up artillery, he thought.

The forested jungle underbrush began to whisper indicating there may be movement along their perimeter. He slow-crawled on his belly toward the hole that seemed to have the most movement out front and quickly realized that it wasn't the enemy that was moving around their lines. It was another huge tiger growling under its breath, patrolling the jungle for food. He knew how much the beast would like to sink those sharp teeth into one of their legs and he wasn't going to let that happen. But as quickly as it came, it disappeared and was gone, quiet permeated everything in a deep black shroud of fear.

As he sat and surveyed his perimeter in the jungle, he heard movement out in the same direction as the first time. He heard a shout coming from up the path and Atlas, the short, blonde headed kid from the Bronx, pulled the pin from a hand grenade and tossed it out into the night's blackness. There was a loud crack, resembling a baseball bat whacking a baseball and dread sank into Roberts' heart. Atlas's grenade had hit a tree trunk returning it back to the sender, everyone sank to the bottom of their holes and he prayed that it would not roll in with him or anyone else.

"Crump," the grenade exploded between his hole and Atlas's, mud and jungle rot showered down, but nobody was hurt except Pig Pen's rubber air mattress which suffered a puncture wound. He could hear Pig Pen cursing as the air left the mattress and he sank to the ground.

It was so dark visibility was zero making it extremely risky to toss a hand grenade out into the invisible trees. He motioned to Skier to get Atlas over to his pos (position) immediately.

Atlas was an excellent Marine, who got his name from Charles Atlas, the famous body builder because that was his passion. He sat in the darkness in shirtless defiance, not against the Lieutenant but in defiance of nature. He owned his mistake; it could have been extremely deadly. In the jungles there is no margin for error, ever, the results of the errors were devastating. After a brief discussion about how unsafe his actions were and what he might do in the future Atlas asked the question that caught Roberts completely off guard.

"Sir, people are going to treat us like heroes when we get back to the World, aren't they? These Charley pamphlets that we've been finding are just a bunch of crap, right, that can't be happening back home. Is it Lieutenant?" His chin pursed up in determination, his thick New Yorker accent rolling from his lips.

Trust, Atlas trusted him to listen impartially and give him an honest answer. Trust is a nebulous gargoyle, difficult to gain, very easy to lose. Leadership is building trust through consistency of actions and behaviors and in combat, both are essential. It requires anticipating circumstances and planning "immediate action," training one's mind to react with spontaneous predictability and consistency.

Earlier in the day as they had approached the NVA hospital, they had discovered communist propaganda leaflets dropped in their path showing peace demonstrations that were happening back home. They showed crowds of protesters by the Washington Monument and the Capital Building in the nation's capital. Unnerving, to say the least, because Roberts knew they were true. Social turmoil engulfed the World they knew, changing it forever.

He could see Atlas's blue eyes glistening in the dark, his young face wrinkled in concern. The Lieutenant's mind slipped back to his trip to Vietnam, eons ago it seemed. Silently he recalled the physical assault on him by the anti-war protesters at the San Francisco bus station. He thought he was going to die, beaten to death by a mob of hippie anti-war protesters but saved by a passing Veteran. The America that he and Atlas knew was no more.

"Look Atlas, remember those pictures that we saw of returning Veterans in New York City riding on vehicles and waving to cheering crowds? That is what you're going to see when you go home, what they're saying is Communist bull!" Although he could barely make out his silhouette in the dark, he could see that Atlas understood his message and more importantly, he wanted to believe it. Atlas apologized for the danger he caused for his fellow Marines and dismissed himself, crawling through the muddy, weedy undergrowth to stand watch the rest of the night. What pride he had in that young man and all the Marines that he was with; they are such a unique group of young man.

The rustling in the night grew louder and seemed to be congregated on his avenue of approach from the Southwest. Suddenly, and unexpectedly, there was a gunshot and the scream. Then the rustling stopped they heard nothing else for the rest of the night. He silently wondered whether the tiger that had been roaming around their lines had finally found some food, the enemy.

Before dawn he passed the word around the perimeter to stand to and they began to move around again. Mosquitoes had indulged on everyone's lips and faces; arms and wrists were swollen from insect bites. A stick that Roberts had spent the night on turned out to be a snake. Some things never change in the jungle.

Dawn is the time of day when they might expect an attack and it was a good way to wake everybody up, get their combat gear on and pay attention to what was happening. Suddenly a tripwire popped silhouetting the outline of four NVA soldiers steadily creeping up to their lines. The machine gun immediately opened up raking the area, killing all four of the attacking NVA and there was silence. Certainly, there were many more NVA around their perimeter, but none were visible. His guess was that farther down the southwest plateau was a staging area where a company size force of NVA were massing for an attack on his position.

"Hogan get on the horn and get some artillery on those prearranged targets. Give them one marker round and we will adjust, then fire for effect." Immediately Hogan was on the radio talking to the fire direction control, lining up the 105's toasting area.

"NVA in the open!" Within minutes he whispered, "shot out" and he could hear a gun in the distance belching its lethal load toward them. Like a hungry freight train, the first spotter round screamed over their heads hitting the positions 200 meters in front of them.

"Right 50." Another shot out and it sounded good.

"Mark it."

"Perfect, fire for effect!" Hell, on wings screamed over their heads again as the battery pounded the hillside back and forth. After 2 shots of 4 rounds each, the silence sucked his breath out and he whispered to Hogan, "Cease fire, I think we're good."

Chapter 4

RIVER OF DEATH

"River of Death." Dung's words slipped into Roberts mind as he looked over the terrain, the river and cliffs. Shivers rushed up his neck, perfect name, he thought.

SOP's (Standard Operating Procedures) would dictate that Roberts dispatch a squad out to assess the damage. As the squad approached the artillery target area, they reported blood trails and body parts of approximately 10 NVA dead. It was a good day for duck hunting, and he ordered the squad back inside their perimeter. The bold move had taken less than an hour and they were ready to proceed on their original mission, but it became increasing apparent to him that they were now going to be out for at least two nights.

Instead of heading west, he decided to travel south along the face of Hill 425N through a gulch and cross the river there. They had driven the enemy west to southwest, and he believed that this way of engaging the enemy would be better than the original route.

The gorge was overgrown with a hint of a steep trail, not well traveled and extremely slippery. In order to keep their footing, they decided on a serpentine path through an area of decaying vegetation, killed by the notoriously toxic herbicide, Agent Orange.

About 250 meters into the hump Turtle raise his right hand to halt. A fireteam fanned out for security and Turtle made his way about 25 meters, to the Lieutenant's position. Automatically, everyone had gone to one knee in a semi-perimeter with weapons at ready.

"Take a look Turtle, make sure we are clear to move down the hill." Turtle and the point fireteam slowly made their approach down the steep hill. As they reached the bottom several shotgun blasts broke the silence. Turtle had run into two NVA and had dropped them both. One was an NVA Lieutenant.

One by one the platoon repelled down the hill hanging on to the vines and vegetation as they dropped. Thank God for their green, nylon jungle gloves. They searched the NVA bodies but found very little intelligence material other than personal pictures and possessions, so they bagged it for the Battalion S-2 Officer. The bodies were buried in shallow graves and they moved ahead.

"Sir, some trip wires up ahead, they are running in a U-shape around our point. I can't tell if they are booby traps or signal flares. What should I do?"

No telling what was connected to them, he thought for a minute, looking at Luke the Puke, trying to determine what he thought. Dung pointed and asked but Luke shook his head with a "probably OK," look. The Lieutenant's educated guess was that it was an isolated, abandoned trip wire but the leader could take no chances. They had to use some of their C4 and blow a hole, so he called up Triggerman, the demolitions expert and explained what he wanted to do.

The patrol reversed course and moved about 30 meters back up the hill and soon there was a whisper up the chain, "Fire in the hole!" Triggerman did the job, the obstacle was cleared, no secondary explosions so they moved ahead, Turtle out front.

About 500 meters down the hill they reached a weed covered plain that led to the river. He could hear the sinister gurgling of the rushing river and quickly saw that it was over its banks because of the Monsoon rains. What normally would have been a 30-meter wade was now a tortuous 45-meter struggle. There was a northward bend downstream between hill 425N and hill

425S, with cliffs on each side. Not a great place to cross but there were no alternatives. Sergeant Skier crawled next to Roberts.

"We need to cross here Skier, what do you recommend?" He was giving the objective and negotiating the details.

"I will have two guys swim across with the rope and secure one end to the other side," explained Skier. As the rain started, he noticed two leaches on Skier's neck, but he was focused on the task and oblivious to him. Why should he know, Roberts thought?

"They can conceal themselves in the weeds. There is a small hill just across the stream that I think we should check out before we get the whole platoon committed, Sir." Good observation and Roberts told Skier so. Grow "good" with praise.

Again, he marveled at how these teenagers stepped forward, two swimming across the river, dragging a rope to tie to the other side so that their buddies could safely cross. What drove them to do these impossible tasks extending beyond anything they would have ever imagined possible?

It was a classic example of pushing beyond one's best and doing what was required. None of these Marines had ever tried to swim across a swollen jungle stream, with a rope and into hostile enemy territory but they went without comment. They wrapped up their gear in ponchos and made floats to keep their weapons dry, tied the ropes around their waists and pushed out into the fast-moving water. The lead Marine stepped into a hole, but he was able to push his floating gear ahead of him and forge on. Remarkable, Roberts thought, great teamwork.

The Marines struggled up the slippery bank, now mud from the rain and tied the ropes to two trees, quickly unpacked their gear and made a quick security check of the area. All was clear, so far, so the remainder of the platoon began their tortuous journey.

He told Hogan to get the coordinates of the hills above the cliffs and register the prearranged artillery targets. With that in place the first squad followed the ropes across the stream. Immediately the first man was swept away by the swift running current but the second Marine caught his arm so he could catch his footing. The water was up to his neck, but both pushed ahead toward the distant bank as torrents of rain dimmed their outline and made them part of the stream.

Soon it was his turn to cross. The current was stronger and colder than he had anticipated, the stream bed was slick with large, slime covered rocks. Roberts' boots caught between two rocks and he started to go under, but Bluto caught him by his pack. As he righted himself, he caught a glimpse of a small truck, submerged, about 100 meters upstream but he couldn't take his attention off of the task of getting across this water beast.

As each squad made it across, they formed an ever-widening security perimeter in what was now a lake until the last squad was across. The deluge mercifully stopped and soon in the distance he could hear the Skyhawk and a helicopter. As the chopper approached, he could see double tires on the front landing gear, an Army CH-47 Chinook. Soon it was gone, rain again.

The Monsoon rain was going to be a problem, no break in sight and now it even drowned out their voices. This would have been a good place to off-load Luke the Puke to the Chinook, but birds don't fly in this kind of weather and they had missed their chance, the low ceiling obliterated the view of the mountains making them impossible obstacles for a speeding helicopter.

Helicopter pilots were a different breed of warriors. If they could possibly fly, they would fly. Regardless of the military organization, they did whatever the situation commanded flying into contested landing zones and in terrible weather. They were remarkable!

Chapter 5

HILL 425S

Luke looked miserable, no head cover, drenched from head to toe but Roberts had to give him credit, he was tough. They were finally at the foot of Hill 425S. They would head 750 meters southwest across the plateau and climb the last 500 meters through a draw to the crest of 425S. The lead fireteam would have to clear a path through the thick grass and bamboo with machetes.

From there they would set up their rally point for the recovery operation. The down-pouring rain was both a blessing and a curse, making life miserable but masking their movements. Sergeant Skier, his face dripping with rain, squinted into Roberts face signaling he was ready to move out, Turtle at point, Hamster, Beachboy, Luke and Dung close behind.

Luke was visibly shaking now, not a common characteristic of the NVA and Roberts wished he knew Luke's story, but he would never divulge anything. Something was up, something was definitely wrong.

The rain stopped and as the lead elements moved across the flat plateau, macheting the thick bamboo and vegetation back, Luke stopped Beachboy, his head shaking no, no, no! In a combination of Vietnamese, English, French and sign language he warned Beachboy that there were NVA machine gun emplacements at the end of the plain. Dung attempted to get more but Luke became tight lipped.

Suddenly several large caliber machine guns ripped through the air. They were on the plateau with neither concealment nor protection, there was no safe place. Then they abruptly stopped, and the rain started again.

Under the Lieutenant's poncho, Roberts and Hogan examined the map, it told him exactly where he would have placed those guns. As the plain began to rise there was a sharp incline, perfect for protecting the eastern avenue of approach to Hill 425S. That was the target.

Hogan called in the coordinates to the FDC (Fire Direction Center) and soon the local freight train roared overhead. Two rounds, perfectly placed, saturated the site, obliterating everything there. They moved to within 100 meters of the impact and Red's squad went ahead to check it out. In the rain and fog the squad looked like ghosts floating toward the high ground.

An M16 opened up on full-automatic on an unknown target, then all was silent, no return fire. The radio cackled, all clear, and the rest of the platoon moved ahead, cautiously, toward the high ground. The Lieutenant was leery, the NVA doesn't stick a machine gun out by itself, there were more, somewhere ahead.

Two enemy RPG's (rocket propelled grenades) exploded to their right close to the stream and he could see the outline of a dozen floppy covers (hats) jouncing up Hill 425S and vanishing into the jungle brush. The M60 machine gun opened up but it was impossible to see the results. They needed more artillery on the position.

They were at the base of the east side of Hill 425S, but their dead Marine comrades were on the west side. They only wanted artillery on the east side, Hogan understood, and the Lieutenant watched the master at work. Hogan adjusted each shot so that he saturated the eastern slope.

The platoon moved out again, rain still pounding like gravel on their steel helmets, the muddy vegetation an ice rink. Hand over hand they grabbed vines and weeds, pulling themselves up the eastern slope of Hill 425S, their jungle gloves indispensable. Although very effective against cuts and certain infections, everyone carried a small bottle of mercurochrome to douse on any skin break regardless of where it was. Youth brought continual facial skin abrasions that required daily doses of the red antiseptic liquid resulting in a war paint appearance. The consequences for not using it was jungle rot, a type of infection resulting from constant infestation from jungle microorganisms.

The slope was steep, not a likely direction of attack so he figured the safest way to advance to the top of Hill 425S. Miraculously, they made it to the top, no resistance or contact with the enemy. Where did Charley go?

"Dung, get Luke back over here pronto!" He wanted to find out what Luke knew. "Ask him where the group of NVA disappeared to, what is around this hill?"

With Dung's coaxing jabs with his knife, Luke was full of information, partly in English. Beachboy and Dung managed to translate Luke's babbling to, "This is large logistical center along the Ho Chi Minh Trail called a Base Area. There are many caves with storage lockers for supplies and a rest area for troops."

"Lieutenant, we are sitting on an NVA city," exclaimed Beachboy! Luke nodded as though agreeing with Dung and Beachboy's assessment. How much English does Luke understand, he wondered?

"Lieutenant, this is an old French minefield." Skier was matter of fact as he whispered the news to Roberts. "Old bouncing mines that we gave the French when they were here."

He showed Roberts the ugly three-pronged triggers attached to the mines buried in a very small mine field along the western slope. The mine field was obvious once he saw where they were positioned, and the Marines were able to mark the few mines that were posing any risk. Just watch where you step Roberts whispered and the caution ran through the Marines. The presence of unseen mines was ghostly.

Again, Hogan set up artillery coordinates and communicated them to the FDC. They were ready. Then Hogan set up air strikes that would be executed the second they stepped off the hill.

"Sergeant Skier, Hogan, let's execute the plan, immediately, so we can get off this jungle coffin!" With the artillery and air support set up, the recovery team assembled on the western slope with Hogan in the lead followed by the recovery team, Roberts next, then Doc. The rain had not let up making it more difficult to locate their dead comrades.

When they were about 100 meters away, Hogan stopped and signaled everyone down. As if in automatic, everyone fell to a knee, weapons pointed out and listened. Hogan checked his map and whispered, "This is it, hit here, we moved toward that rise. This is our rally point."

Before they moved to the objective, the Lieutenant made radio checks with all the support, artillery, air and helicopter. As they had planned and practiced, the Lieutenant, Hogan, Doc and now, due to their casualties Pig Pen and four Marines headed for the bodies of their fallen Marines while the rest of the platoon formed a hasty perimeter, their base camp so to speak, and waited.

Finally, they reached the objective, two brothers laying side by side, defending each other beyond life. An eerie stillness settled in, nobody said a word, they had found their Marines and they needed to get them home.

"Oh, man," whispered Pig Pen, "Don't mean nuthin, don't mean nuthin."

Doc had taken two body bags and quickly they slipped their brothers into the bags and zipped them up. Flies immediately covered the dark body bags; the jungle had already started to reclaim them, but they had beaten the maggots.

They would be pall bearers in the gruesome, surreal world of Vietnam and their dead comrades' families were waiting. With two men to a bag, the young Marines carried them back toward their rally point, their granite faces holding in the pain.

After identifying their dog tags again, Hogan called the medevac helicopter to the designated pickup site and they headed toward the coordinates. It would take a while for the birds to arrive from the combat base, none were in the air and if it was still storming at the landing strip, they wouldn't take off anyway. Additionally, it would be a bit tricky because he did not want to pop a spotter smoke grenade. Suddenly, the rain stopped, and the sun came out, a miracle orchestrated by fate. A medevac chopper would be available to fly and make the extraction.

According to plan, the platoon formed a perimeter around the jungle extraction point and Hogan stood by the dead Marines, his friends, his family. The dual rotary bird, a CH-46, sounded like a circus in a Greyhound bus, its rotors screaming its arrival. Like a giant grasshopper, it crept toward their position, Hogan on the radio, a small mirror flashing sunlight back to the chopper. Slowly, so slowly, it hovered reverently overhead, dropped the jungle penetrator down and carefully, almost tenderly, reeled in one body bag at a time.

It was mid-afternoon when the platoon headed back toward the Company position on Hill 555, mission accomplished. But it was becoming clear to Roberts that they did not have enough daylight left to make it back to the Company position, so he decided to return to the area around Hill 425N for the night. The NVA would be waiting for them at the first stream crossing point so instead of retracing their steps to the east, he headed north where they found a suitable fording. After making a safe crossing, they headed up the western slope of Hill 425N, the side that they had hit with artillery earlier.

Chapter 6

Night Terror

As they reached the western slope of Hill 425N, in his mind Roberts could imagine the rounds tearing into the enemy facilities and crushing what enemy guarded it. He almost smiled but felt it inappropriate.

Turtle began to discover the fresh graves; 12 total NVA had been killed by the artillery strikes. Good hunting! The trees were limbless, torn to bits by the incoming 105 rounds. Blood trails were everywhere, indication that the enemy had removed their dead and wounded and only chunks of anonymous human flesh remained.

Protocol would tell them to dig up the graves and glean intelligence from the bodies, but they didn't have time and it was risky staying in one spot for long. There was also the distinct possibility that the graves were booby trapped. In this environment movement was safety, so they humped the trail toward the top of hill 425N.

By now they were completely drenched in sweat, dirt stuck in the creases of their faces making them look like old men. The putrid smell of rotting jungle vegetation filled the young Lieutenant's nose making him feel like an old man, weary and wise beyond his years. Vietnam did that to people, accelerated the days so that at the end of a year tour, one's body had just seen a lifetime of experiences, the horror permanently engraved in their minds.

On they pushed toward Hill 425N and as the sun began to set, Sgt. Skier moved close to Roberts. "Sir, I think we should find another night position. We know what might be on hill 425 and by the time we get there it will be after dark."

Good idea, they were too far from the Company perimeter to make it back before nightfall, so Roberts and Skier looked over the map for a suitable night position. They selected another defendable position to the northwest of hill 425N. The interesting aspect of this particular hill appeared to be more of a plateau on the map but was in fact a defendable hill.

Roberts had noted it the night before. Now, how would I attack it, he thought as he worked through several plans for setting up his defense? He was always evaluating situations in terms of how he would attack them, looking for cover and concealment and vulnerability.

It was far enough away from the higher elevations to avoid enemy defilade fire and the military crest was small enough that they could form a perimeter for the night with their drastically reduced platoon. Additionally, it lent itself well to artillery support. The eastern slope was almost a cliff, so they concentrated the defense on the trail and the other slopes.

The military crest is below the topographical crest. It is a position where the Marines could see their fields of fire and they were not silhouetted against the sky, their background was the hill side. The topographical crest was the point of highest elevation, both had their advantages and disadvantages.

The platoon arrived at their objective just before dusk, set up a defensive perimeter and rested. Skier positioned each foxhole and the machine gun with good fields of fire. It was imperative that they position the trip flares and Claymore mines to compensate for their lack of numbers. Sergeant Skier was an expert at stretching the defensive positions to appear as if they were at maximum strength.

While Skier was positioning the platoon, Hogan made contact with their artillery support. They registered six prearranged artillery targets around their perimeter making sure they marked and communicated their exact position. The smoking lamp was out, no cigarettes to give away their position. About 25 meters down the trail they put out one LP with a radio, a risky move but they didn't know where the NVA might be and Roberts was sure they were following close behind.

The Marines dug in for the night carefully placing the trip flares on their own and Roberts was once again overcome with pride for these teenagers who were under his command, no; they had each earned the right to be called men now. They had performed their tasks with no complaints, each willing to give up their lives for their brothers. They portrayed an overwhelming sense of camaraderie, possible only under the worst of conditions, which is what this hazardous mission had imposed on all of them. Roberts felt how lucky he was to be in command of such a wonderful group of men – he would never forget them nor would he allow anyone else to forget them. These were real men.

A half-moon and a sky full of stars made it easy to see but the trees of the jungle limited the distance. One had to fight a feeling of claustrophobia, it was like the trees were continually closing in, pressing, and never allowing a minute's rest. A million eyes hid behind the green, mossy trunks, piercing the confidence that had accumulated during the daylight.

Roberts allowed his mind the luxury of roaming the sky looking for familiar constellations or planets and thinking of home, fighting off despair. Dig deep within for strength, his Dad had told him. The sky was the same, a bit skewed, but all there. Roberts took solace in the fact that his wife and son could be looking up at the very same sky, even though it was not night back home, but it felt homey for him to think of them on the other side of the world.

He had barely dispersed his platoon into their night defensive positions when the enemy came in waves. Trip flares burned as RPG's hit the perimeter, green tracers from the NVA AK-47's knitted the air in neat dots, inches from his head. They were surrounded by dancing green uniforms that blended into the foliage like ghosts, the round tops of their helmets bobbing as they came. Screams and constant small arms fire built into a deafening roar, they were inside his lines, shooting, screaming and killing. In the flashes of blasts, he could see his Marines, illuminated as though flash bulbs were stopping them in motion, tackling the little NVA and stabbing them, shooting them, choking them. His Marines fought like devils, died like the heroes that they were.

The defensive line was over-run and his mind panicked, where could he run to be safe? The Angel of Death was breathing on Roberts naked neck, whispering panic in his ears, dark wings caressing his helpless shoulders. Where are you God, I need you!

Roberts could hear someone screaming and realized it was his own voice, operated by an unknown demon of fear. His hands were shaking uncontrollably quickly infecting his neck and back. His shoulders grew cold with fear, but it quickly passed when he realized he was responsible for his own safety.

He emptied his Colt 1911 .45 pistol into a crowd of nobody's, then grabbed his M16. It jammed after one shot, misfeed out of the magazine, in his haste he must not have fully seated the magazine. Doesn't matter, it was a good club.

"Hogan, call in the artillery, now!" It was their only hope, their last resort, artillery on his own position. He willed his heart to quit thinking, this was not going to be pretty.

"Barnyard, Barnyard, this is Porkchop One, fire mission, over!" Hogan was using his Recon call sign.

"Porkchop One this is Barnyard, say again, over!" The FDC, the Fire Direction Center for the artillery battalion in support of Roberts mission came back immediately but gabbled.

"Barnyard, I have you Lima Charley (phonetic alphabet for LC or Loud and Clear), Hotel Mike (HM or How Me)? Over." Hogan was checking to see if the FDC could hear him well enough so that there were no mistakes.

"Porkchop, Barnyard, have you Lima Charley, over."

The attack only lasted minutes, but suddenly the NVA were all gone, either dead, wounded or alive; they all retreated like a green wave pulls seaweed into the ocean's anonymity. The attacking survivors were dragging their dead and wounded with them as they withdrew past the still burning trip flares and taking Luke the Puke with them. His Marines had beaten the enemy back but at what cost? The Lieutenant could hear the screams, the moans, the terror, as he crawled around making sure they still had their line secured.

Luke was gone but Dung lay still, his reddish hair moving with the wind, three large holes in his chest from his former comrades, killing him instantly.

But was that the purpose of the attack, retrieve Luke? Who was Luke that they would commit that many casualties to get him back?

"Hogan, artillery, call it onto their route of departure." They needed to secure their position. "Get Medevacs in here, emergency Medevacs." The collective knowledge was mind boggling.

"Triggerman, get the C4 and blow these trees, make an LZ so we can get a basket in here." Triggerman was a miracle worker. He had the C4 connected to the blasting caps and detonation cord before Roberts could determine his casualties.

"Fire in the hole!" A makeshift landing zone appeared.

"Sergeant Skier, how many hit?" He didn't want to know but he had to know.

"Three K's and twelve W's. Six will have to be evacuated."

The cost was three Marines and Dung, the Kit Carson Scout, killed with twelve wounded. In less than 10 minutes the Lieutenant had lost almost half of his Marines, but he took some solace in the fact that the attackers could have completely wiped them out had they really intended to. But why Luke, who was he?

"Medevac on the way Sir, should be here in minutes!" No sooner than the words had left his mouth he could hear the Sea Knight, tearing at full speed toward their position. Hogan flashed a signal light and Bluto talked him in. The chopper's landing lights illuminated the LZ. The LZ looked too small but the pilot was incredible, fitting the dual rotors between the trees, no basket needed.

Against the prop wash, Hamster and Yacker assisted the wounded as they were loaded into the rear bay, then the limp ponchos holding their dead. As the last body was carried on board the prop wash caught the corner of the poncho revealing the face of one of his most respected Marines. Turtle's face looked at peace, he was finally heading home, his dream of being an American citizen gone. Sweetness and Carson lay lifelessly, next to him, quiet, also ready to go home with Dung next to his friends. Roberts mind took over, shut up heart, I don't need you right now.

On this night a part of him died along with his young Marines. They stood for everything that is great about American youth, he was humbled in their presence as he looked over their poncho covered bodies. All he could think of was their families and friends back home, not knowing the truth, yet.

The Jungle returned to a velvet darkness, no outlines, nothing but quiet. His Marines! What a group of fabulous young men they were, motivated by faith in each other and pride in their Corps. They would let neither down.

The survivors of the attack dug foxholes into the rock mountain forming a new defensive perimeter. Bluto and the Lieutenant dug a two-man hole on the perimeter with the rest of the platoon, instead of their normal position behind the lines and the night began. Before midnight Roberts made a hole check of each position to make sure everyone was awake. He returned to his hole and let Bluto take over watch and sitreps (situation reports.) He needed a moment of rest.

Atlas took over the machine gun. Captain Grog would be happy, it worked perfectly, and it was clean.

Scorpions swarmed Roberts' legs and feet and jungle rats crawled on his arms and neck. Glad to see some things don't change in the jungle, he mused to himself. Then he heard it, or more accurately felt it. Heavy stomps in the valley south of their position along their stream. The stomps picked up pace and soon it became clear it was an Arclight, a B-52 bomber flight probably out of Guam and making the bombing run on Hill 425S that they had ordered. But the concerning part was it was stomping directly toward their position on the hill.

It was a continuous explosion now, like an arc welder drawing a bead, the darkness gone, and bomb shrapnel ripped through the trees on their position as Roberts bounced in harmonic cadence. What were they doing? Were the maps that bad? Was their navigational equipment off, they were halfway between Hills 425N and 425S?

As quickly as it started, it was done, quiet except for the waning noise from the B-52 bombers jet engines as they headed home. Rain began again filling the holes with muddy water, their luxury accommodations for the night. They were about 1,100 meters from the rest of their Company, it would be good to get home.

Chapter 7

HILL 555

The next morning, they left their position on Hill 425N and made an uneventful hump to Hill 555. As they made their way through the Company perimeter, they were greeted by the CO.

"Good job Lieutenant, welcome back!" He accomplished his mission, reclaiming the dead Recon Marines but was not returning with all of his Marines. ordinary teenagers, now experienced combat veterans. They had snickered in the face of death. How he loved these extraordinary Marines and what an appalling cost they paid for our freedom. Roberts promised that he would ensure that they would never be forgotten.

Three horrific days out of thirteen months. One can begin to understand that this is the ultimate price that Veterans pay for our FREEDOM.

Chapter 8

CONCLUSION

In combat, safety is essential and psychologically one must be ready to accept the consequences of their decisions. In one's mind, those outcomes can be mitigated with the understanding that you have trained your team to be the best and you have trained your mind to immediately assess situations, break them down into problems and solve them.

Effective leaders prepare their minds by constantly creating a potential set of circumstances so they will quickly react in real situations. Indecision or delay will undermine morale, lead to poor execution and feelings of guilt.

Some will say there is a problem with America's youth, that they are unmotivated and self-centered. America's youth will do what it is asked, the problem is what we ask for.

Semper Fidelis is a Latin phrase that means "always faithful." A common greeting between Marines is "Semper Fi" recognizing the sacred oath between all those who have served America under the Eagle, Globe and Anchor. Is this what drove this group of young Marines to accomplish the impossible?

Semper Fi expresses the pride and love for each other, love for their families and a deep obligation to their country. They were fueled by loyalty to a common cause, always faithful to their relationships, always meeting the challenges and expecting others to push them to do better. Ordinary teenagers, now extraordinary Marines bonded by an ancient slogan, Semper Fidelis, Always Faithful.

Failures never defined them, bouncing back from each altercation over and over and reapplying the hard-earned details to the next challenge. It was also about assumptions and expectations.

They assumed that each Marine would do their part, expecting others to always push them to exceed their past best.

Semper Fidelis embodies the virtues necessary for Freedom to thrive. With that understanding, they continued to accomplish incomparable feats, understanding that their best efforts were never enough. The Marines continually completed what the challenges demanded.

America's youth has always stepped up to the challenges to our freedom. But, the power of these two words inspired these young Americans to travel thousands of miles from home, alone, to fight an unpopular war, living for months at a time in the degrading filth of the jungle. To them it was simple. They served because their country asked them to and they believed in your Freedom to choose. Semper Fidelis, Always Faithful to the mission at hand, to their fellow Marines, to their country and to your freedom.

Keep in mind, today's social media requires neither physical presence nor physical courage. Veterans have courageously given us the gift of FREEDOM, defending it with their lives so that we can make our own choices. It is our sacred duty as Americans, to accept this gift by displaying the physical courage to make <u>responsible choices</u>. Freedom is a precious gift to us all. It is the gift of choices, to follow our dreams. As each of us follows our dreams, others can build on each other's accomplishments and make their dreams work.

Veterans are excellent sources for help in making the right choices. They can be resources in Responsibility and Accountability, Pride, Planning and Failure. Their experience highlights the fine line between Consistency and Discord. Here are some ideas.

Responsibility and Accountability

Responsible Americans can make the best choices when they look at themselves and realize that they are responsible for themselves. Freedom is a result of holding oneself accountable for their actions, on their own. Adults don't blame others and don't try to explain failures. Veterans will not ask you what happened, those are only excuses, but why did you let that happen? Their experiences tell them that not keeping commitments has cataclysmic consequences. When they promise, they deliver and when you promise them, they hold you accountable for your word.

Pride and Best Effort

Veterans take pride in their experiences, relationships and their organizations knowing the importance of building pride in others. Pride builds a self-confidence seldom garnered from other emotions and creates an optimistic view of one's environment. They take pride in organizations that inspire them to rise above their past best and do what the conditions demand.

Planning and Failure

When one puts his or her life on the line, one quickly learns that missing the smallest detail leads to disastrous results. Success comes from good planning, leadership, communication and adapting to ever-changing environments. Veterans never let failure define them but learn and grow.

Integrity and Discord

Integrity takes on a whole new meaning with a Veteran and one that can be very valuable because lives hang in its grip. They know that inconsistency leads to conflict and disasters. They see Integrity as keeping your mind and what it thinks, your heart and what it feels and the relationships you keep all be in sync, working together. Discord leads to an indecisive choice.

Put the iPhone down and personally engage a Veteran. They can seem cranky and reticent, but they can provide invaluable guidance and the implications of poor choices, just ask them! You may be surprised to learn that their guidance is not about the horrors of war but about being responsible for yourself and making good life selections.

A popular phrase now is "Thank you for your service," when people want to recognize a Veteran. Veterans appreciate the intent of "thank you for your service," but Veterans gave you a gift and you have accepted it by living in America. So, Veterans would rather hear,

"Thank you for my FREEDOM," because you are worth it.

TAKE THE PLEDGE

- **I am responsible for myself and accountable for my behaviors.**

- **I will not be defined by failure and I will never quit.**

- **I will never settle for my best effort.**

- **I will create a supportive environment where my friends build pride and confidence in each other.**

- **I will always balance my mind and heart.**

Made in the USA
Middletown, DE
21 August 2021